TODAY'S CHAR HITS
Playalong *for* Alto Saxophone

Wise Publications
part of The Music Sales Group
London/New York/Paris/Sydney/Copenhagen/Berlin/Madrid/Tokyo

Published by
Wise Publications
14-15 Berners Street, London W1T 3LJ, UK.

Exclusive Distributors:
Music Sales Limited
Distribution Centre, Newmarket Road, Bury St Edmunds,
Suffolk IP33 3YB, UK.
Music Sales Pty Limited
120 Rothschild Avenue, Rosebery, NSW 2018, Australia.

Order No. AM997139
ISBN 13: 978-1-84938-027-0
This book © Copyright 2009 Wise Publications,
a division of Music Sales Limited.

Arranging and engravings supplied by Camden Music.
Edited by Fiona Bolton.
Compiled by Nick Crispin.

Printed in the EU.

CD recorded, mixed and mastered by Jonas Persson.
Backing tracks arranged by Danny Gluckstein.
Alto Saxophone played by Howard McGill.

www.musicsales.com

Your Guarantee of Quality:
As publishers, we strive to produce every book to
the highest commercial standards.
The music has been freshly engraved and the book has been
carefully designed to minimise awkward page turns and
to make playing from it a real pleasure.
Particular care has been given to specifying acid-free, neutral-sized
paper made from pulps which have not been elemental chlorine bleached.
This pulp is from farmed sustainable forests and was
produced with special regard for the environment.
Throughout, the printing and binding have been planned to
ensure a sturdy, attractive publication which should give years of enjoyment.
If your copy fails to meet our high standards,
please inform us and we will gladly replace it.

www.musicsales.com

Saxophone Fingering Chart

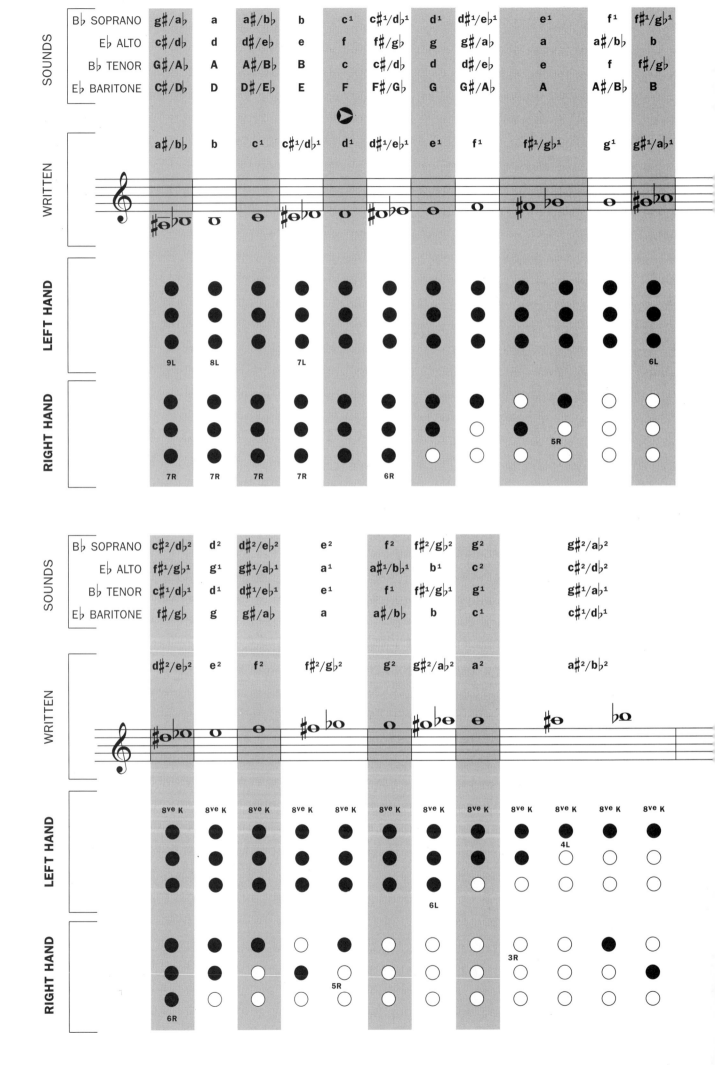

Indicates the lower limit of the best playing range

Indicates the upper limit of the best playing range

LIGATURE

MOUTHPIECE

CROOK

THUMB SUPPORT

BODY

1L

4L

2L
3L
1ST FINGER

5L
2ND FINGER
3RD FINGER
6L
7L
8L
9L

LEFT HAND

OCTAVE KEY

THUMB REST

1R

2R

3R

*4R

1ST FINGER

5R

2ND FINGER

3RD FINGER
6R

7R

RIGHT HAND

THE RING

* Not fitted on some saxophones

Apologize (OneRepublic)

Words & Music by Ryan Tedder

Chasing Pavements (Adele)

Words & Music by Adele Adkins & Francis White

The Fear (Lily Allen)

Words & Music by Lily Allen & Greg Kurstin

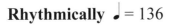

Hallelujah (Alexandra Burke)

Words & Music by Leonard Cohen

Expressively ♩. = 61

mp cantabile

cresc. poco a poco

f

mf espressivo

mf cantabile

f

mf espressivo

molto rall.

Human (The Killers)

Words & Music by Brandon Flowers, Dave Keuning, Mark Stoermer & Ronnie Vannucci

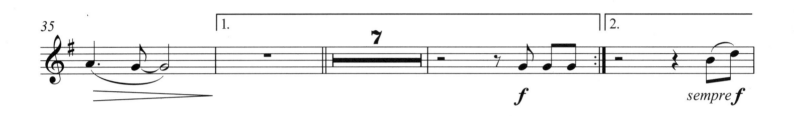

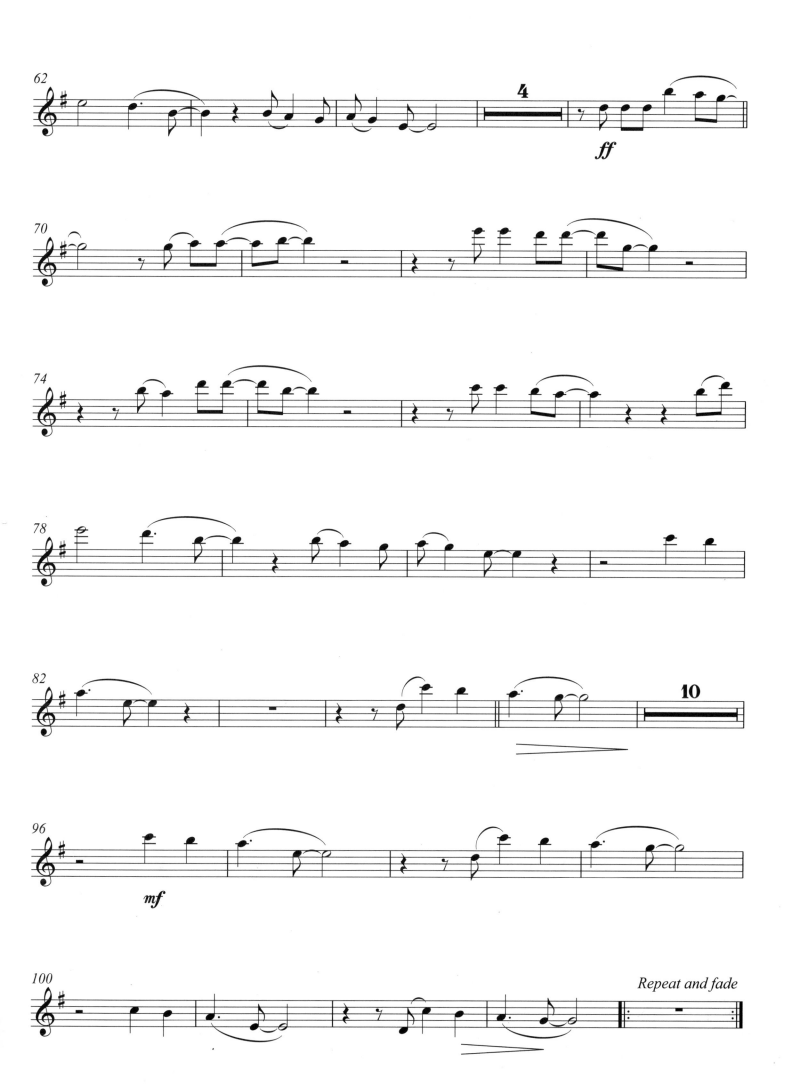

Warwick Avenue (Duffy)

Words & Music by Duffy, James Hogarth & Eg White

Relaxed and controlled ♩ = 84

If I Were A Boy (Beyoncé)

Words & Music by Beyoncé Knowles, Tobias Gad & Britney Carlson

to Coda ⊕

mp

mf

D.S. al Coda   ⊕ **Coda**

f

Rule The World (Take That)

Words & Music by Mark Owen, Gary Barlow, Jason Orange & Howard Donald

Run (Leona Lewis)

Words & Music by Gary Lightbody, Jonathan Quinn, Mark McClelland, Nathan Connolly & Iain Archer

Viva La Vida (Coldplay)

Words & Music by Guy Berryman, Chris Martin, Jon Buckland & Will Champion

CD1 Track Listing

1. **Tuning notes**

   Full instrumental performances...

2. Apologize
   (Tedder) Sony/ATV Music Publishing (UK) Limited.

3. Chasing Pavements
   (White/Adkins) Universal Music Publishing Limited.

4. The Fear
   (Allen/Kurstin)Universal Music Publishing/EMI Music Publishing Limited.

5. Hallelujah
   (Cohen) Sony/ATV Music Publishing (UK) Limited.

6. Human
   (Flowers/Keuning/Stoermer/Vannucci) Universal Music Publishing Limited.

7. Warwick Avenue
   (Duffy/Hogarth/White) EMI Music Publishing Limited/Universal Music Publishing Limited/ Universal Music Publishing MGB Limited.

8. If I Were A Boy
   (Gad/Knowles/Carlson)EMI Music Publishing Limited/Cherry Lane Music Limited/ Universal/MCA Music Limited.

9. Rule The World
   (Owen/Barlow/Orange/Donald) EMI Music Publishing Limited/Sony/ATV Music Publishing (UK) Limited/ Universal Music Publishing Limited.

10. Run
    (Lightbody/Quinn/McClelland/Connoll/Archer) Kobalt Music Publishing Limited/Universal Music Publishing BL Limited.

11. Viva La Vida
    (Berryman/Martin/Buckland/Champion) Universal Music Publishing MGB Limited.

CD2 Track Listing

1. **Tuning notes**

   Backing tracks only...

2. Apologize

3. Chasing Pavements

4. The Fear

5. Hallelujah

6. Human

7. Warwick Avenue

8. If I Were A Boy

9. Rule The World

10. Run

11. Viva La Vida